the source

arrangements for worship groups

book 3

B♭ instruments

arranged by Chris Mitchell

Kevin
Mayhew

We hope you enjoy the music in this book.
Further copies of this and the other books in the series are available
from your local music shop or Christian bookshop.

In case of difficulty, please contact the publisher direct:

The Sales Department
KEVIN MAYHEW LTD
Rattlesden
Bury St Edmunds
Suffolk IP30 0SZ

Phone 01449 737978
Fax 01449 737834
E-mail info@kevinmayhewltd.com

Please ask for our complete catalogue of outstanding Church Music.

First published in Great Britain in 1998 by Kevin Mayhew Ltd.

ISBN 1 84003 130 1
ISMN M 57004 213 5
Catalogue No: 1470309

0 1 2 3 4 5 6 7 8 9

Cover designed by Jaquetta Sergeant.

Music arrangements by Chris Mitchell
Music Editor: Donald Thomson
Music setting by Chris Mitchell and Vernon Turner

Printed and bound in Great Britain

Contents

This index gives the first line of each hymn. If a hymn is known by an alternative title, this is also given, but indented and in italics.

CHRIS MITCHELL is a well-established arranger, composer, musical director and session musician who has worked with Graham Kendrick, David Peacock, Gloria Gaynor and the BBC. He and his wife, Linda, are experienced worship leaders and are involved in providing seminars and workshops for Christians in the arts.

the source will be developed into a major resource for the churches. It is already available in the following editions

Words Only	ISBN	1 84003 121 2
	Catalogue No.	1470101
Full Music	ISBN	1 84003 120 4
	ISMN	M 57004 204 3
	Catalogue No.	1470104
Complete Acetate Masters	ISBN	1 84003 119 0
	Catalogue No.	1470201

Arrangements for Worship Groups:

Book 1 for C instruments	ISBN	1 84003 122 0
	ISMN	M 57004 205 0
	Catalogue No.	1470301
Book 1 for B♭ instruments	ISBN	1 84003 128 X
	ISMN	M 57004 211 1
	Catalogue No.	1470307
Book 2 for C instruments	ISBN	1 84003 123 9
	ISMN	M 57004 206 7
	Catalogue No.	1470302
Book 2 for B♭ instruments	ISBN	1 84003 129 8
	ISMN	M 57004 212 8
	Catalogue No.	1470308
Book 3 for C instruments	ISBN	1 84003 124 7
	ISMN	M 57004 207 4
	Catalogue No.	1470303
Book 3 for B♭ instruments	ISBN	1 84003 130 1
	ISMN	M 57004 213 5
	Catalogue No.	1470309

201 I cry out for your hand

(Good to me)

Craig Musseau

202 If you are encouraged

Graham Kendrick

2 verses

Verse

Chorus

203 I give you all the honour
(I worship you)

Carl Tuttle

3 verses

Majestically

Verse

Chorus

to verses　　　　*last time*

204 I have come to love you

Matt Redman

3 verses

205 I have made you too small
(Be magnified)

Lynn DeShazo

2 verses

206 I heard the voice of Jesus say (Tune 1)

Traditional English melody

3 verses

206a I heard the voice of Jesus say (Tune 2)

John Bacchus Dykes

3 verses

207 I just want to be where you are

Don Moen

208 I just want to praise you

Arthur Tannous

209 I know a place
(At the cross)

Randy and Terry Butler

210 I know it

Darlene Zschech

211 I lift my eyes up to the mountains
(Psalm 121)
Brian Doerksen

212 I lift my hands
(I will serve no foreign god)
Andre Kempen

213 I love to be in your presence
Paul Baloche and Ed Kerr

214 I love you, Lord, and I lift my voice

Laurie Klein

With feeling

215 I love you, Lord
(Holy is your name)

Mike Day and Dave Bell

216 I love your presence

Fabienne Pons

217 I'm accepted, I'm forgiven

Rob Hayward

218 I'm gonna click

Capt. Alan J. Price

4 verses

219 Immanuel, O Immanuel

Graham Kendrick

Worshipfully, but with strength

220 Immortal, invisible, God only wise

Traditional Welsh hymn melody

5 verses

221 I'm so secure
(In your hands)

Reuben Morgan

2 verses

222 I'm special

Graham Kendrick

223 I'm standing here to testify
(Come to the light)

Kevin Prosch

2 verses

224 I'm your child

Richard Hubbard

3 verses

225 In Christ alone

Shawn Craig and Don Koch

226 I need you more

Lindell Cooley and Bruce Haynes

21

227 In every circumstance

David Fellingham

With a 12/8 feel

228 In heavenly armour
(The battle belongs to the Lord)

Jamie Owens-Collins

3 verses

229 In moments like these

David Graham

230 In my life, Lord
(Lord, be glorified)
Bob Kilpatrick

Prayerfully

231 In the morning when I rise
(All I want)
Andy Park

232 In the presence of a holy God

Mark Altrogge

2 verses

233 In the secret

Andy Park

2 verses

234 In the tomb so cold
(Christ is risen!)

Graham Kendrick

Triumphantly

4 verses

235 I reach up high

Judy Bailey

2 verses

236 I receive your love

Paul Armstrong

2 verses

237 Is anyone thirsty?

Graham Kendrick

238 I see the Lord

Chris Falson

239 I sing a simple song of love
(Arms of love)

Craig Musseau

Gently, with feeling

240 I sing praises

Terry MacAlmon

2 verses

241 Is it true today
(History maker)

Martin Smith

242 Isn't he beautiful

John Wimber

2 verses

243 I stand amazed in the presence

Charles H. Gabriel

5 verses

244 I stand before the presence

Mavis Ford

245 I stand before your throne

Matthew Ling

2 verses

246 I, the Lord of sea and sky

(Here I am, Lord)

Dan Schutte

3 verses

Verse

Chorus

D.C. last time

247 It is to you

Duke Kerr

248 It's our confession, Lord
(Sweet mercies)

David Ruis

249 It's rising up

Matt Redman and Martin Smith

3 verses

250 It's your blood

Michael Christ

251 I've found a friend
(Joy in the Holy Ghost)
Russell Fragar

2 verses

252 I've got a love song

Matt Redman

5 verses

253 I walk by faith

Chris Falson

254 I want to be a tree that's bearing fruit
(I want to be a blooming tree)

Doug Horley

to repeat   *last time*

255   I want to be out of my depth in your love

Doug Horley and Noel Richards

Gently

Fine

D.S. al Fine

256 I want to serve the purpose of God
(In my generation)

Mark Altrogge

4 verses

257 I went to the enemy's camp
(Enemy's camp)

Richard Black

258 I will be yours

(Eternity)

Brian Doerksen

259 I will build my church

Graham Kendrick

260 I will change your name

D.J. Butler

261 I will dance, I will sing
(Undignified)

Matt Redman

262 I will enter his gates
(He has made me glad)

Leona von Brethorst

With pace and swing

263 I will lift my voice

Geoff Bullock

2 verses

264 I will never be the same again

Geoff Bullock

265 I will offer up my life
(This thankful heart)

Matt Redman

2 verses

Gently

266 I will praise you all my life
(O faithful God)

Mark Altrogge

267 I will seek you

Matthew Lockwood

268 I will seek your face, O Lord

Noel and Tricia Richards

2 verses

Worshipfully

Chorus

269 I will wave my hands

Ian Smale

270 I will worship
(You alone are worthy of my praise)
David Ruis

2 verses

Worshipfully, with strength

271 I worship you, Almighty God

Sondra Corbett

272 I worship you, O Lamb of God

Graham Kendrick

2 verses

273 Jesus, at your name
(You are the Christ)

Chris Bowater

274 Jesus Christ
(Once again)

Matt Redman

2 verses

Thoughtfully, not too fast

275 Jesus Christ is Lord of all
(Jesus is our battle cry)
Graham Kendrick

2 verses

276 Jesus Christ is risen today
from *Lyra Davidica*

3 verses

277 Jesus Christ is the Lord of all

Steve Israel and Gerrit Gustafson

278 Jesus, God's righteousness revealed

(This kingdom)

Geoff Bullock

2 verses

279 Jesus, how lovely you are

Dave Bolton

4 verses

Worshipfully

Chorus

280 Jesus! I am resting, resting

James Mountain

4 verses

281 Jesus, I am thirsty

(More of you)

Don Harris and Martin J. Nystrom

With feeling

282 Jesus is greater

Gill Hutchinson

283 Jesus is King

Wendy Churchill

4 verses

284 Jesus is Lord!

David Mansell

3 verses

285 Jesus is the name we honour

(Jesus is our God)

Philip Lawson Johnston

3 verses

286 Jesus, Jesus
(Holy and anointed one)
John Barnett

With feeling

287 Jesus, Jesus, Jesus
Chris Bowater

Worshipfully

288 Jesus, Jesus, you have the name
(Hearts on fire)
David Hadden

289 Jesus' love has got under our skin

(Under our skin)

Graham Kendrick

290 Jesus, lover of my soul

John Ezzy, Daniel Grul and Stephen McPherson

291 Jesus, name above all names

Nadia Hearn

292 Jesus put this song into our hearts

Graham Kendrick

5 verses

293 Jesus reigns

Colin Owen

3 verses

294 Jesus, remember me

Jacques Berthier

295 Jesus, restore to us again

Graham Kendrick

5 verses

296 Jesus shall take the highest honour

Chris Bowater

297 Jesus, take me as I am

Dave Bryant

298 Jesus, the name high over all

Thomas Phillips

6 verses

299 Jesus, we celebrate your victory

John Gibson

2 verses

300 Jesus, we enthrone you

Paul Kyle